STEIN'S
ANIMAL LIFE

FOR THE LAST TIME... WHO PUT THE
DOG BISCUIT ON SEVENTEEN?

DON'T BE SILLY MARTHA ! THEY'RE JUST LEMMINGS !

WHO GETS THE BEER IN THE BOWL ?

OF COURSE YOU CAN SERVE IT WITH THREE PARTS OF GIN AND AN
OLIVE, IF HE INSISTS, BUT GENERALLY THE DROPS ARE JUST
MIXED INTO THE DOGFOOD. . .

IT'S QUITE A RARE SPECIMEN... A VENTRILOQUIST PARROT !

BY THE WAY - WHAT'S A CHORD?

ANY KIND OF PIZZA IS FINE — WE
ONLY WANT TO WOLF DOWN THE
DELIVERY BOY ANYWAY!

LET ME GET THIS STRAIGHT...
YOU WANT A WAKE - UP CALL FOR MARCH ?